Shining
His
Light

A Faith Legacy Journal
Roger Sonnenberg

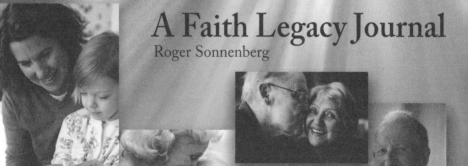

*The LORD is my light
and my salvation.*
Psalm 27:1

The mission of CTA is to glorify God
by providing purposeful products that
lift up and encourage the body of
Christ—because we love him!

www.CTAinc.com

Shining His Light:
A Faith Legacy Journal

by Roger Sonnenberg

Copyright © 2011 CTA, Inc.
1625 Larkin Williams Rd.
Fenton, MO 63026

Printed in Thailand
ISBN: 978-1-935404-34-7

Shining His Light

rnaling accomplishes many things. Recording our stories . . .

helps us realize anew how good God has been to us. As we recall our Lord's work in our lives, it stirs up thankfulness in our hearts. The joy of thanksgiving then shines from our lives. It radiates in our words and actions.

makes it possible for us to shine Jesus' love into the hearts and lives of the next generation. Perhaps your writings will stir up questions in young people who look to you for guidance and wisdom. This, in turn, can spark conversation in which the light of Jesus shines even more brightly.

can open opportunities to shine the light of Christ into the lives of friends and neighbors. Maybe you can recruit some friends to form a journaling group—and share Jesus' love with each other. Hearing the stories others tell may help you recall details of your own, details forgotten over the years.

this journal to talk to Jesus. As you review the Bible verses listed on each e, you will hear God speak to you in them. In turn, you can speak to your Lord rayer, writing your prayers and your memories down on these pages. And you look for ways to tell others what you've discovered—shining his love into their s.

er Jesus rose from the dead, he spent time with his disciples. Two of them said ne another, "Were not our hearts burning within us while he talked with us on road and opened the Scriptures to us?" (Luke 24:32). May the Savior bless you he same way with his presence and peace as you spend time with him, listening is Word and witnessing to his love by writing and speaking about the light t brightens life now and forever.

A record of the genealogy of Jesus Christ the son of David, the son of Abraha
Abraham was the father of Isaac, Isaac the father of Jacob,
Jacob the father of Judah and his brothers.
Matthew 1:1–2

A family tree gives people a concrete understanding of who they are and where they came from. Use the family tree on this page to jot down names and relationships from your earthly family—as many as you can remember.

Try This	Identify those on your family tree who confess Jesus as Savior. Offer a prayer of thanks that their lives shine with the light of Christ. Circle the names of those who are still alive and are not believers. Spend some time praying for them.

ese are written that you may believe that Jesus is the Christ, the Son of God,
and that by believing you may have life in his name.
John 20:31

most people *Jesus* is simply a name. What gives the name Jesus
aning is his story. Pretend that a friend has never heard of Jesus and
 has asked you to explain who Jesus is and what it is about him that
kes you love him so much. What would you say to her? Record your
wer below. (If you like to sing, why don't you sing, "I Love to Tell the
ry," as you write the story?)

_____

_____

_____

_____

_____

_____

_____

_____

_____

Some people spend years working on their family
tree. They can name ancestors, going back for
multiple generations, but too often they do not
know the stories that accompany those names.
Stories inspire. They give hope. Which person | Try
on your family tree has a story you hope the | This
next generation will remember? Shine the light
of Christ by telling that story to someone in the
next generation.

The Word became flesh and made his dwelling among us. We have seen hi..
glory, the glory of the One and Only, who came from the Father,
full of grace and truth.
John 1:14

John reminds us that Jesus ("the Word") became flesh and came to dwe..
in our midst. He came with "grace and truth." As you think of these tw..
words, what people and events from your lifetime come to mind? Recor..
your thoughts below.

_____

_____

_____

_____

_____

_____

_____

_____

_____

_____

Shining His Light

By faith Noah, when warned about things not yet seen, in holy fear built an ark to save his family. By his faith he condemned the world and became heir of the righteousness that comes by faith.
Hebrews 11:7

Noah spent years building an ark simply because God told him to do so. He trusted and obeyed (Genesis 6–8). Reflect on how this one event—the building of the ark—changed Noah's life and the lives of those around him. It was what we call a "turning point."

Most people are where they are today as a result of 4 or 5 turning points. Record the turning points in your life below (for example, the birth of a child, the death of a loved one, a job relocation). Think about each. How did Jesus use each to change the course of your life and make you the person you are today? Choose one turning point and write about it.

_____

_____

_____

_____

_____

_____

_____

_____

_____

_____

Esau said to his father, "Do you have only one blessing, my father? Bless me too, my father!" Then Esau wept aloud.
Genesis 27:38

For a variety of reasons, some children believe they have never met the standards set by their parents. Often, these children spend a lifetime trying to earn the blessing of their parents or other authority figures. It's nothing new. Genesis 27 records the sad example of Esau who lived thousands of years ago.

How good it is to know that everyone who confesses Jesus Christ as Lord and Savior lives under the blessing of God. Jot down some of the blessings for which you are most thankful. Begin each sentence with the words, "Because of Jesus, I . . ."

_____

_____

_____

_____

_____

_____

_____

_____

Shining His Light

Know therefore that the LORD your God is God; he is the faithful God, keeping his covenant of love to a thousand generations of those who love him and keep his commands.
Deuteronomy 7:9

ost people who recall their stories see a larger picture of their lives than ose who do not take time to journal. As you write your stories and ead them, you will likely see God's faithfulness in a fresh way. You will ely see anew ways the light of Jesus' love transformed your life. Look ck at the turning points you listed on page 7. Write about one that allenged your trust in your Lord. What happened? What did Jesus ch you?

_____

_____

_____

_____

_____

_____

_____

_____

_____

Think about God's faithfulness in your life. Remember the times you've doubted his faithfulness. Pray that God will help you trust him more. Who might be open to listening to you speak about this? How could you shine the light of Jesus' love into that person's life?

Try This

For no matter how many promises God has made, they are "Yes" in Christ.
2 Corinthians 1:20

We can rely on every promise God has made to us. How do we know that? The resurrection of our Savior proves it. Just as he promised, he died for us and on the third day rose from the dead for us. Now we can know for certain that God will keep every other promise he has made, too.

Write about one of the turning points you listed on page 7. As you write, reflect on God's faithfulness to you in it.

_____

_____

_____

_____

_____

_____

_____

_____

_____

Try This	Besides forgiveness for our sins, what other promises from God are you sure he will keep? Make a list. After each promise, write a big "AMEN," meaning, "for sure!" Phone someone who needs to hear one of these promises today, and share it!

Shining His Light

Remember the wonders he has done, his miracles,
and the judgments he pronounced.
1 Chronicles 16:12

hroughout Scripture, we are encouraged to remember the marvelous orks of God. When we reflect and remember, it's hard not to radiate, to : the love of our Savior shine through us into the lives of others. Look ck at page 7 and the list of turning points there. Write about one of ese, reflecting on ways you experienced God's marvelous love for you.

Finally, brothers, whatever is true, whatever is noble, whatever is right, whatever is pure, whatever is lovely, whatever is admirable—if anything i̇ excellent or praiseworthy—think about such things.
Philippians 4:8

The things we focus on usually affect the way we feel. Philippians 4 encourages us to think about things that are "true . . . noble . . . right . . . pure . . . lovely . . . admirable . . . and praiseworthy."

In the last few pages of this journal, you've written about a handful of significant turning points in your life. Today, write about any of those you listed on page 7, but have not recorded so far. In your conclusion, note tḣ "true, noble, right, pure, lovely, admirable, or praiseworthy" outcomes of that turning point.

_____

_____

_____

_____

_____

_____

_____

Try This	Put a pad of sticky notes in a drawer next to your bedroom mirror. Each day, ask yourself, "For what do I want to thank Jesus today?" Write down one thing each day and post it next to the mirror.

Shining His Light

These days should be remembered and observed in every generation by every family.
Esther 9:28

tudies tell us that family traditions create closeness. They give family embers a sense of belonging, of identity. Family traditions promote a nse of safety and security in a world that often seems to be ever anging and chaotic.

ist 3 to 5 special days you think every generation, every family should member. Why? What have previous generations done to remember ese days (for example, worship practices, decorations, a family barbeque, atching football together)? Which observances do you enjoy most?

_____

_____

_____

_____

_____

_____

_____

_____

_____

_____

_____

What, then, shall we say in response to this? If God is for us, who can be against us? He who did not spare his own Son, but gave him up for us all— how will he not also, along with him, graciously give us all things?
Romans 8:31–32

In Romans 8:31–39, the apostle Paul asks a series of questions and answers them. In your own words, summarize the first question (above). Then think back to everything you've written so far in this journal. How would you answer his question? How do your experiences show that if God is for us, nothing can defeat us?

_____

_____

_____

_____

_____

_____

_____

Try This	Think of someone who needs to hear the promises of God from Romans 8—a shut-in, a new widow, a person who has received bad news. Choose a way to shine Christ's love and hope into that person's life. Then telephone, e-mail, or send a note reminding that person of God's promise and of your prayers for them in the situation.

Shining His Light

Who will bring any charge against those whom God has chosen?
It is God who justifies.
Romans 8:33

"Will you be in heaven someday?"

Some people answer that question by saying, "I sure hope so," or "I'm trying to get there." Christians are not "hoping to get to heaven" or "trying to get there." We know God has given us eternal life—right now—as his gift. When our life here on earth ends, the eternal life he has given us will continue as we meet our Savior face-to-face in heaven.

Review some of the Bible verses that promise this (for example, Isaiah 53:4–5; 1 Peter 2:24; 2 Corinthians 5:21). Then pretend a friend with a terminal disease has just asked you, "What happens to me when I die?" In the space below, record your answer to the question. Does anyone you know need to hear the answer for real? How could you share it?

_____

_____

_____

_____

_____

_____

_____

_____

Who is he that condemns? Christ Jesus, who died—more than that, who wa[s] raised to life—is at the right hand of God and is also interceding for us.
Romans 8:34

Pretend you're in a courtroom. The judge is God himself. The devil is th[e] prosecutor. He is making the case that because of your sins, you deserve [to] live apart from God forever. Jesus is your defense attorney. Journal the words he might be speaking in your defense. Based on Romans 8:34, wh[at] do you imagine him saying about you? What will the judge's verdict be? How do you feel about that?

_____

_____

_____

_____

_____

_____

_____

_____

_____

_____

_____

Shining His Light

> *Who shall separate us from the love of Christ? Shall trouble or hardship or persecution or famine or nakedness or danger or sword? . . . No, in all these things we are more than conquerors through him who loved us.*
> Romans 8:35–37

's hard to believe Christ's love could be so persistent. Could God really ove people like Adolf Hitler or Saddam Hussein? The truth in this pas-ge from Romans 8 (above) is clear. We can reject God's love, but we an't stop him from loving us. Try drawing a picture of this truth without sing words. Then write about a time when you separated yourself from od's love (for example, your college years). What did you feel during at time? How did God lead you back to himself? Write about it.

Read the story Jesus told about the forgiving father from Luke 15:11–32. Do any parts of Jesus' story remind you of your own experiences as a prodigal? As you think about this, thank God for the ways his love shone into your life and brought you back to himself.

Try This

These commandments that I give you today are to be upon your hearts. Impre *them on your children. Talk about them when you sit at home and when you* *walk along the road, when you lie down and when you get up. Tie them as* *symbols on your hands and bind them on your foreheads. Write them on the* *doorframes of your houses and on your gates.*
Deuteronomy 6:6–9

What truths did God want the Israelites to remember? Why do you thin they kept forgetting?

If you were to write down five truths you want the next generation to know and treasure always, what would they be? Write them below. Then pray that each one of these truths might become meaningful in the lives of your children, your nieces and nephews, and/or other young people yo care about. Ask the Holy Spirit to teach you how to shine these truths more brightly from your own life into theirs.

_____

_____

_____

_____

_____

| Try This | Think about some of the truths you've learned about Jesus, perhaps from a parent or from the friend whose words led you to faith. Have you forgotten some of them? If so, why? |

Shining His Light

I pray that the eyes of your heart may be enlightened in order that you may know . . . his incomparably great power for us who believe. That power is like the working of his mighty strength, which he exerted in Christ when he raised him from the dead.
Ephesians 1:18–20

this passage, St. Paul is speaking about resurrection power. Before e resurrection of Jesus, the greatest power known on earth was God's eative power. The Creator spoke and the universe sprang into existence.

esurrection power is even greater than that! Resurrection power brings e out of death. That new life is now at work in you! Write about a ne when you experienced Christ's power at work in you. For example, rhaps after a significant job loss or the death of a spouse or a child, you ought you could not go on, but Christ's sustaining love at work in you rried you through the grief and brought you safely to the other side.

_____

_____

_____

_____

Sometimes counselors hear people say, "I just can't . . ." One counselor makes Christian clients rephrase, changing the "I can't" to "I won't." He believes that with God, all things are possible. List some of your "I can'ts" on a slip of paper. Then cross them out and print, "I won't." Better yet, change them to "I can with Christ's help."

Try This

"For I know the plans I have for you," declares the LORD, "plans to prosper yo
and not to harm you, plans to give you hope and a future."
Jeremiah 29:11

These words come from the Old Testament. God was already making plans to send the Messiah, the world's Savior. That Savior would bring forgiveness and life eternal to all who believed. God kept that promise— in Jesus Christ and in his cross and empty tomb. There, the love of God shines most brightly!

Do the words of promise bring comfort to you still today? Why? Journal about that.

_____

_____

_____

_____

_____

_____

_____

_____

_____

Try This	Pray, thanking God for his plans to love and save you even before you were born. Then talk with him about the hopes he has in mind for your future.

Shining His Light

This is what the LORD says: "Stand at the crossroads and look;
ask for the ancient paths, ask where the good way is, and walk in it,
and you will find rest for your souls."
Jeremiah 6:16

hat do you think God means when he talks about the "ancient paths"?
hat pathways were good for your ancestors? Have you found them to
equally good for you? What "rest" has Jesus brought to your soul? (See
atthew 11:29.) Journal about that in the space below.

When King Herod heard this he was disturbed, and all Jerusalem with him.
When he had called together all the people's chief priests and teachers of the
law, he asked them where the Christ was to be born. "In Bethlehem in Judea"
they replied, "for this is what the prophet has written."
Matthew 2:3–5

The chief priests and scribes knew where to find the Christ Child, but they didn't go to worship him. For many Christians, Christmas is one of the most worshipful times of the year. They understand it's not so important how much you spend on Christmas. What counts is the way you spend Christmas.

Write about Christmas traditions you have enjoyed over the years. What traditions have helped you see the Christ Child most clearly and worship him most meaningfully? Think of a way to share one of them with a child you love.

_____

_____

_____

_____

_____

_____

_____

ɔve is patient, love is kind. It does not envy, it does not boast, it is not proud. is not rude, it is not self-seeking, it is not easily angered, it keeps no record of wrongs. Love does not delight in evil but rejoices with the truth. It always protects, always trusts, always hopes, always perseveres. Love never fails.
1 Corinthians 13:4–8

w descriptions of love compare with that in 1 Corinthians 13. Here, e apostle Paul describes God's love—a love that gives, a love without nditions. In the space below, draw a cross. Then write about what God's ʾe shown in the cross of Christ has meant to you throughout your life.

_____

_____

_____

_____

_____

_____

_____

_____

_____

_____

_____

He is not here; he has risen!
Luke 24:6

Easter is the most joyous festival of the Christian year. The resurrection
our Lord is essential for our Christian faith. Read 1 Corinthians
15:12–22, noting everything that would be different if Jesus had not bee
raised from death.

Then think back on the Easter celebrations you've enjoyed. Write about
one that for you was especially memorable and joyous. What made it so?
If you have space, include some family Easter traditions. Include enough
so that if someone from a future generation reads your words, they'll
know how to repeat that tradition.

_____

_____

_____

_____

_____

_____

_____

_____

_____

Shining His Light

esus said, "If you hold to my teaching, you are really my disciples. Then you will know the truth, and the truth will set you free."
John 8:31–32

1 July 4 each year, citizens of the United States commemorate the ning of the Declaration of Independence by the Continental Congress Philadelphia in 1776. America was born. It was a land of new edoms, where men and women had the opportunity to speak and rship as they desired.

st the country (or countries) from which your ancestors came. If you ow any of the stories they told about coming to the U.S. from another untry, write about them. (The stories may even be your own!)

_____

_____

_____

_____

_____

_____

_____

_____

_____

_____

Now listen, you who say, "Today or tomorrow we will go to this or that city,
spend a year there, carry on business and make money." Why, you do not even
know what will happen tomorrow. What is your life? You are a mist that
appears for a little while and then vanishes.
James 4:13–14

Though we do plan for tomorrow, tomorrow remains uncertain. Many
things could happen that would change any plans we make. Write about
time when you worried about tomorrow and all the worry turned out to
be a waste of energy.

_____

_____

_____

_____

_____

_____

_____

_____

_____

Try This	Share a piece of advice about tomorrow with someone in the next generation.

Shining His Light

I have not stopped giving thanks for you, remembering you in my prayers.
I keep asking that the God of our Lord Jesus Christ, the glorious
Father, may give you the Spirit of wisdom and revelation,
so that you may know him better.
Ephesians 1:16–17

his passage records Paul's prayer for the Christians in the city of
hesus. He asks that God will give them the "spirit of wisdom and
velation, so that [they] might know him better." What knowledge about
od makes a person truly wise? Whom did the Holy Spirit use in your
e to help you know God better (for example, a godly mother, pastor,
cher)? List some of these people in the space below and summarize
w they helped you. Then list names of people you want to encourage
their faith, lives into which you hope to shine Christ's peace.

_____

_____

_____

_____

_____

_____

_____

_____

_____

_____

I pray also that the eyes of your heart may be enlightened in order that you may know the hope to which he has called you.
Ephesians 1:18

Scripture often uses the word *hope*. When it does, it means more than wishful thinking (for example, "I hope I get that special gift at Christmas time"). Instead, hope as Scripture uses it is a certainty.

A very ill person wrote a special Christmas letter to his family. It said three things: 1) Life is difficult, 2) God is merciful, 3) Heaven is sure.

Is there someone in your life who is experiencing difficulties in life and needs to know that God is merciful and heaven is sure? If so, plan a way to shine the hope Christ brings into that person's life. Then write a note or make a phone call to share the hope that is ours in Jesus!

_____

_____

_____

_____

_____

_____

_____

_____

Shining His Light

ray also that your heart may be enlightened in order that you may know . . .
the riches of his glorious inheritance in the saints.
Ephesians 1:18–19

hat comes to mind when you hear about the "riches of [Christ's]
rious inheritance"? Certainly, heaven! However, Paul is also talking
out us! We are God's saints, his precious people, his children through
th. We are his ambassadors. We are the "salt of the earth" and a "light
those in darkness." Jesus willingly gave up his life to purchase you
himself!

rite about a time you weren't confident in God's love. What kind of
ference does it make to know God thinks so highly of you?

_____

_____

_____

_____

_____

_____

_____

_____

_____

_____

_____

I am torn between the two: I desire to depart and be with Christ, which is better by far; but it is more necessary for you that I remain in the body.
Philippians 1:23–24

Sometimes older people will ask, "Why am I still here on earth? What purpose do I have? Why doesn't God just take me?"

When we feel that way, we need to remember that God makes no mistakes. He doesn't walk away, leaving us and forgetting about us. If you're still on earth, he still has a purpose for you! Think about the people who surround you. How might God be using you to make a difference in the lives, to shine through you with his hope and peace? How might you wa to make that difference? Write about it in the space below.

_____

_____

_____

_____

_____

_____

_____

_____

_____

Shining His Light

[Je]sus said,] *"Do not let your hearts be troubled. Trust in God; trust also in me. [In] my Father's house are many rooms; if it were not so, I would have told you. [I a]m going there to prepare a place for you. And if I go and prepare a place for [yo]u, I will come back and take you to be with me that you also may be where [I a]m. You know the way to the place where I am going." Thomas said to him, ["L]ord, we don't know where you are going, so how can we know the way?" Jesus answered, "I am the way and the truth and the life. No one comes to the Father except through me."*

John 14:1–6

[Jes]us was leaving his disciples. He knew he would soon be put to death [for] the sins of the world. His love for his followers—including us—moved [him] to speak these final words to them. What assurance does he give [the]m? What assurance do you take from his words?

[In t]his journal's closing entry, write a letter to your spouse, family, or [frie]nds. Include your closing thoughts. What would you like them to [kno]w and remember? What feelings would you like to express? Think of [you]r letter as a way to shine the light of Jesus' love into their lives.

Shining His Light

_____

_____

_____

_____

_____

_____

_____

_____

_____

_____

_____

_____

If this book has made a difference in your life or if you have simply enjoyed it, we would like to hear from you. Your words will encourage us! If you have suggestions for us to consider as we create books like this in the future, please send those, too. Send e-mail to editor@CTAinc.com. Please include the subject line: SGL1PJ.